T R A F F I C

2011-12 NMI
MISSION EDUCATION RESOURCES

❊ ❊ ❊

BOOKS

AFRICAN DREAMS
Church Growth in the Horn of Africa
by Pat Stockett Johnston

FOOTPRINTS ON THE DOOR
Fifty Years in Papua New Guinea
by Bruce, David, and Brendan Blowers

NOTHING STANDS IN OUR WAY
by Brian Utter

PAUL ORJALA
The Man, the Mission
by R. Franklin Cook

TRAFFIC
Sold into Slavery
by Bruce Nuffer and Darrell MacLearn

VISTAS
The Changing Face of Nazarene Missions
by R. Franklin Cook

❊ ❊ ❊

NEW ADULT MISSION EDUCATION CURRICULUM
Living Mission
Vol. I, Part 1: Forgotten People
Vol. I, Part 2: Forgotten People

T R A F F I C

Sold into Slavery

BRUCE NUFFER AND **DARRELL MACLEARN**

Nazarene Publishing House
Kansas City, Missouri

Copyright 2011
Nazarene Publishing House

ISBN 978-0-8341-2570-4

Printed in the United States of America

Editor: Aimee Curtis
Cover Design: Kevin Williamson
Interior Design: Sharon Page

10 9 8 7 6 5 4 3 2 1

AUTHORS' NOTE

One question storytellers get as much as any other is, "Is that a true story?" Generally the person asking the question means, "Are those factual details exactly as they occurred in real life?" But there are other truths that may be more important than the order of events.

When you read this book, if what you mean by this question is, "Is there a girl named Lupita with a sister named Natalia?" you are asking the wrong question. If instead what you really want to know is, "Is this really how a sex slave is abducted? Is this how she is transported? Does she move around this much? Is life really this bad?" or dozens of other similar questions, the answer is an unequivocal "Yes, this is really a true story."

CHAPTER 1

As night fell, the rain came in from the west in angry needles of white as Lupita crouched in the damp corner of her family's shanty. She sat in crowded loneliness, lost in her thoughts as she listened to the howling wind.

Lupita's uncle Cesar grinned at her, but she didn't notice. For fifteen years he had been glaring at her—the grin should have caught her attention. His feelings weren't a secret; with nineteen other family members sharing mattresses and food, he felt Lupita should be bringing in more money to help the family. But if she had seen the look in his eyes today, she would have seen something different—something darker and more resolute in that so-called grin.

The next morning, Lupita awoke as her uncle nudged her with his boot.

"Let's go," he said. "We've got a special trip today."

Since coming to live with their uncle five years earlier, Lupita and her younger sister were expected to pull their weight and help feed the family. School had to take a backseat to work, and she assumed today would be no different. Each day Lupita and her sister went to work in her family's market stall in Guatemala City's Plaza Mayor. But today *was* different.

"Where are we going?"

"Today your life begins, girl. You can thank me later," he added with a smile in his voice, turning and heading for the jeep.

With the sun rising in their eyes, they drove east toward town. The only time Lupita spoke was to ask again where they were going, to which Cesar only smiled and said, "It's a surprise." Lupita wisely wanted nothing to do with any surprise Cesar had in mind.

Before long they headed into neighborhoods where the buildings no longer looked condemned, and the stores had real windows and doors. Cesar turned down a wide, quiet street, soon stopping in front of a cozy-looking home.

She looked at her uncle quizzically. He chuckled, "I told you it was a surprise. Come on." Before they reached the front door, a heavy middle-aged woman came out. She smiled and greeted them.

"Hola, Lupita. Me llamo es Señora Ramirez," she said, motioning for everyone to come inside. The woman led Lupita and her uncle to a comfortably decorated room and invited Lupita to make herself at home while she and Cesar talked in another room.

For nearly half an hour Lupita tried to read a magazine, only to find herself staring out the window wondering what Cesar meant by "today your life begins." Soon she heard a distant door open, and the low voices of her uncle and the woman wafted into the room. She waited for them to come back; eventually the woman returned alone. She barely had time to wonder where her uncle was when she glanced him placing a wad of something in his hip pocket as he went out the front door.

The woman read the surprise in Lupita's face. "Don't worry," she laughed, heading through the room to what Lupita had seen was a kitchen. "You have much better things to think about now that you have a new job! Would you like a drink?"

Thoughts and worries multiplied in Lupita's mind. Why did her uncle leave? Why hadn't anyone told her about this new job? What kind of new job did she have? Who was this woman, and why was Lupita in her home? Who would watch out for her sister? Since their mother's death, Lupita had become

Natalia's comfort and protection from the cruel extended family they now lived with.

From the other room came the sound of cabinets opening and closing, the clinking of glasses, the pouring of liquid.

"What kind of job? Housekeeping?" Lupita finally managed to ask, beginning to think she was this woman's new hired help.

"It all depends," said the woman, returning from the kitchen with a coffee cup and a glass of soda. She handed the soda to Lupita. "There are many kinds of work to be done. Today, you just relax and do whatever you want. Come on, I'll show you to your room."

The woman led Lupita down the hallway where she'd gone earlier with Cesar, and pushed open the door to a large bedroom.

"I see you don't have any clothes with you," said the woman. "Check the closet, and help yourself to whatever fits. I'm expecting more girls throughout the day. Why not take a shower and get cleaned up. Just let me know if you need anything."

The woman padded back down the hallway, while Lupita just stood looking at the large room. It was nearly as big as her family's entire house! It had two large beds, with thick quilted blankets and numerous pillows. There was even a dresser with a television set on it. Lupita opened the closet and stared at a dozen dresses in different sizes, jeans, and blouses of all kinds. Many of the items still had department store tags on them.

As she sat on the edge of the bed, her mind felt numb. *Is this a dream? What in the world is going on?* Last night she crouched in a broken-down hovel wondering what she had done to deserve such a life. And today it was as if her prayers had been answered in miraculous fashion. It couldn't be real.

Despite her suspicions and the fact that she felt like a thief, Lupita did what she was told. In the bathroom were several packages of new undergarments and a stack of towels. She started a bath. Once the warm water began flowing over her, she noticed the tiredness creeping into her body.

As she bathed, Lupita heard adult voices come and go up and down the hallway outside the bathroom. She heard Señora Ramirez instructing someone else about the clothing in the closet. As she drained the water, Lupita wondered how many others would arrive today, and she surprised herself when a sickly tremor tickled her spine. As nice as the bath was, and as exciting as the new clothes should have been, for a fifteen-year-old girl in her situation it didn't take a genius to realize something wasn't right.

CHAPTER 2

The uneasy feeling stayed with Lupita all day as several more girls arrived. Some of the girls were clearly younger than Lupita—maybe ten or eleven years old—and two looked several years older, maybe as old as nineteen or twenty. Despite their differences, they all had narrow, darting eyes and tense, alert bodies.

At lunch in the kitchen Señora Ramirez set out a big tray of *empanadas*, a bowl of *frijoles*, and cans of soda. She laughed when the girls all looked too shy to take any, so she began handing out paper plates piled with food.

"You girls don't look like you're on vacation! Really, just relax. How about some entertainment while we eat?" She led the girls to the large front room and, choosing from a stack of DVDs, inserted a comedy to lighten the mood. "Feel free to eat in here if it's more comfortable for you."

The movie seemed to relax everyone. By the time it was over, several of the girls had dozed off, and others were even beginning to smile. As the credits began to roll, one of the girls selected another DVD and put it into the player. This went on for several more hours before Señora Ramirez finally announced an end to the day.

Before they went to sleep, Mrs. Ramirez handed each girl a plastic bag and instructed her to place the clothes she was currently wearing in the bag when she dressed in the morning. The girls were to carry the bags with them.

As the girls settled in for the night, their nervousness returned. They gave each other timid glances, and some questioned aloud what would happen the next day.

CHAPTER 3

Lupita woke to the smell of scrambled eggs and *chorizo*. She noticed the pallets of some of the other girls were empty, and she sat up slowly, trying to piece together this whole strange experience.

In the kitchen, several of the girls had already dressed in their new clothes and sat eating eggs with their bags of old clothes at their sides. Following their lead, Lupita helped herself to breakfast, then dressed and sat in the living room, staring vapidly at something on the television while she waited for her future to arrive.

It was barely late morning when the doorbell rang, and Señora Ramirez let in two serious-looking men. She greeted them with a nod, then turned and led them down the hallway. It was the last time Lupita ever saw her.

A few moments later one of the men reappeared and announced loudly, "Get your things and be outside in two minutes." The girls exchanged silent glances as if asking one another, "Do we really go with them?" before tentatively stepping onto the front porch with their bags.

Outside, two minivans rested in the driveway, each with a woman in the front passenger seat. The man who had directed them outside began assigning the girls to the vans. Once they had been evenly divided between the vehicles, they got in and the vans pulled out, Lupita's stomach tightening.

The woman in the front seat of Lupita's van addressed the girls.

"We will be flying out of Guatemala City today, and it is very important that you listen to my instructions." The woman began removing several large plastic bags from a duffle bag at her feet. She read what was written on each one, and as she passed them out she continued, "These are your passports and travel visas. You must have them to be able to fly. Once we have passed through the check-in area, you will return them to me for safekeeping."

Lupita took a bag and wondered how these people whom she had never met had this book with her name and picture in it. The riot of emotions twisted in her stomach as she moved further and further away from anything resembling her life. She'd never flown on a plane. She'd never left Guatemala City. Had she been with her sisters, it would have felt like Christmas. But as it was, she felt more like a character in a joke before the punch line hits.

The airport was a whirl of frenzy, with Lupita trying to stay connected with her group as the man and woman led them through the crowd—a crowd of persons focused on their own individual destinations and totally unaware of what was happening right in front of them. Lupita had half a mind to slip away, but she was curious about the job her uncle had mentioned, and she was excited to fly in a plane. So before she knew it, she was seated in a jet with four other girls, and her passport and travel visa had disappeared back into the black duffle bag.

For most of the flight the girls slept or read the magazines in the seat-back pockets. Lupita sat next to a younger girl, April, and together they shared their short, nearly identical stories. April was twelve and had come from an area east of Guatemala City. Her mother had died when she was younger, and she lived with relatives who farmed vegetables. A neighbor had brought her to Guatemala City to Señora Ramirez's house because he said her family had found a job for her in the United States working at a restaurant. He said she'd earn enough money to live and have extra to send back to her family.

After nearly three hours, the plane brought the girls to an airport on the edge of a desert town. Besides knowing that she was somewhere in Mexico, Lupita had no idea where she was. The woman with the girls' travel documents quickly herded them out of the airport and into a parking garage where they met two men leaning against a large new pickup truck. The straight-haired man with the mustache was barely taller than the bed of the truck, but the other man—dressed in a cowboy shirt and boots— was almost as tall as the truck itself.

As the girls approached, the men smiled and rose to meet them. Neither of the men looked at the woman with the duffle bag but instead gazed lecherously at the girls, looking them over intently.

"Right on time," the first man announced to the woman. "As usual." He handed her a thick envelope.

The woman thumbed through a stack of American money in the envelope before adding, "And a perfect deposit, just as expected." She smiled at the men as she turned and walked away. "They're all yours."

The girls watched in desperation as the woman headed back toward the airport. One girl called after her and took a step in her direction, but the short man caught her upper arm before she had taken two steps.

"Easy there," he breathed, holding her arm in a steel grip and pulling her close. "You belong to us now. We paid good money for you." He let his eyes wander slowly down her body. He leaned his face close. "I hope you are worth it," he whispered.

CHAPTER 4

Darrell MacLearn sat in the front seat of the Expedition next to his friend and fellow abolitionist Michael Hanson. It hadn't taken them long to visit six massage parlors and one adult entertainment center where prostitution and possibly modern-day slavery were active. They recapped what they had learned so far and made plans to leave the crowded parking lot and visit one more massage parlor on their way to the cantinas.

It had been a short drive from Michael's house, and within minutes he was pointing out the small buildings with neon call signs pointing the way to massage parlor brothels. Pulling into the parking lot of a strip mall the neon sign read *Asian Paradise, Stress Management*. This was the seventh brothel, the seventh place within a mile radius where primarily Asian women were trapped between lust and greed. The seventh place where "massages" would be paid for and sexual services would be expected.

As they entered the spa, no one noticed anything unusual about the two men. They were husbands and fathers, and they looked no different than all the other men who had been serviced that night—except their lives were dedicated to eliminating the world's second-largest criminal enterprise rather than fueling the need for more victims of human trafficking.

Michael, the director of outreach for the Houston Rescue and Restore Coalition, was a veteran in the abolitionist movement. Having mapped out most of Houston's sexually oriented businesses, he spent his days finding new ways to enlist helpers in the fight.

Darrell, the project manager of Concerned Women for America's sex trafficking obliteration project in Texas, spent his days working to end the demand for commercial sex and thus the need for a steady supply of boys and girls to fill the cantinas, strip clubs, tea rooms, and massage parlors.

Asian Paradise, Stress Management was no different than the other six locations: dark red and pink colors, neon lights, security cameras, a small foyer waiting room, gated doors and darkened windows, seductively dressed Asian women behind an interior window with a money exchange opening, and a sickening mix of fragrances and perfumes. Each place had the same atmosphere of guilt and shame mixing with the fragrances of seduction and greed. The secrecy was evident by the turned heads of men as they quickly exited the buildings without making eye contact.

"So, before we head to the cantinas, let's debrief. What did you notice?" Michael asked.

"Emptiness. I noticed emptiness in their eyes," Darrell said, as the faces flashed through his memory. Michael headed toward another part of town where they would find cantinas that were known Mexican brothels.

Entering Houston's port area, the process started over. Michael drove slowly, pointing out cantinas and bars and talking about the port and the part it plays in human trafficking. Pulling into the dark, empty parking lot of a recently raided bare wooden cantina across from the railroad tracks, Michael began to explain some things to look for and expect. "Ready?" he finally asked.

"Ready as I'll ever be. Let's do it." Darrell replied, with both determination and apprehension.

The parking lot was always full on Saturdays at La Costenita Cantina in Houston's port area. Tonight was no different. Cars were double-parked in front of the building, and the two men waited at the entrance to the side lot for the parking attendant to direct them where to park.

"Notice anything unusual about that fence?" Michael asked, pointing to a tall wooden fence running alongside the building.

"Should I?" asked Darrell.

"It's a corridor," said Michael. "It's a path to that building out back where the girls in many cantinas work and sleep. This one in particular has an escape hatch in the side of it in case of unwelcome visitors. This allows the girls to exit the building and head out over the tracks." Michael continued with a motion of his head toward the darkness behind the building.

As they approached the armed bouncers at the front doors, Darrell realized how serious the cantina was about protecting their investments.

"Arms out to the side," commanded the first bouncer, flicking his cigarette into the pebbled parking lot.

Michael and Darrel stood spread-eagled while the bouncers patted them down in search of weapons. Then with a nod of his head the men were welcomed in.

Immediately inside the front doors were two busy pool tables and a bar that was lined with men and their "dates." In the center of the room was an empty dance floor, surrounded by small square tables. The conversations around the room were muted by the energetic Spanish music coming from the small band at the edge of the vacant dance floor.

"Feels like a bad high school dance," Darrell snickered.

Seductively dressed girls lined the wall waiting for a "date." Some sat and drank $14.00 beers while others turned on the charms and followed their date's lead and desires.

Michael and Darrell sat at a table, and before long a girl approached Michael. "Hola. Cómo está, Maria?" asked Michael, smiling. He turned to Darrell and explained, "These women make money by getting men to buy them drinks. The fee for their time with the men is wrapped into the price of the drink. The more drinks they can sell the more they make. Unfortunately, most of these girls will never see most of that money. Some people call it debt bondage, which is just another way of calling it slavery, pure and simple."

Darrell nodded his head in understanding and began to look into the eyes of the girls around the room while Michael turned his attention to Maria.

Maria had met Michael before in the cantina, and they had talked on several occasions. She knew he was not the normal cantina client. He was kind and gentle and, without creating a scene, worked hard to send a message of hope to those he visited with. She demonstrated moments of trust as she talked about her four-year-old son whom she had not seen for two-and-a-half years, and how she was working hard and hoped to see him again someday.

As they left the cantina that night, with the thoughts of Maria's son and the face of this young mother etched into his memory, Darrell's resolve and commitment was solidified.

CHAPTER 5

As the truck drove away from the airport, Lupita and April held hands. The man's words echoed in Lupita's head, "We paid good money for you." All her life she had lived in one of the world's most dangerous cities, always watching, always wary of Guatemala's mafia that operated near the Plaza Mayor where she sold her family's fruit. Now she had been snared, and it was dawning on her that her own uncle had been the one who committed her to this new hell.

One of the youngest girls began to cry, softly at first, trying to stem the increasing tide of tears with her hands. But it was useless—the tears came faster and harder. The tall man who was driving cursed at her, and added, "I'm not listening to that all the way to our destination. You have exactly one chance to be quiet." When she wouldn't stop crying, the driver pulled the truck off the shoulder and the short man got out. He yanked open the door to the rear cab and threw the young girl to the ground. As she tried to stand, he swung his foot into her stomach. The force of his kick raised her torso and sent her spinning backward where she slipped on a patch of gravel, landing again on her face. Before she could get up, the man was on her back, severely twisting her right arm to the back of her neck.

"We don't have time to repeat ourselves, or patience for you to decide to listen. We have only one rule: obey or die. Shall I assume you want to live?"

"Yes," the girl choked out between sobs.

The man lifted her with her arm still pinned behind her back. "I thought so. Now get back in the truck!"

Years later Lupita realized this was the point when her voluntary hold on reality first began to slip. In increasing fits and starts, she would gradually give herself over to a life of fantasy where only her imagination could sustain her. And, as she would find, there were many times when imagination wasn't nearly enough.

x x x

It was early afternoon when the truck finally stopped in front of a large woodpile. They had arrived at what appeared to be a lonely, dusty ranch. Broken corral fencing surrounded empty, weed-laden plots of ground. In the distance stood a tall, freshly painted barn that appeared to have been made into some sort of restaurant. The dirt parking lot was large, and tall windows flanked the front of the building on opposite ends.

In the other direction sat a sprawling two-story wood and stucco house. The varying degrees of weathered paint and opposing architecture made it appear as if someone had expanded the home on multiple occasions. The men led the girls into this building.

The front room looked like any normal home, with a couch and chairs and a large television set. The tall man pushed in front of the girls and moved down the hallway. "This way," he directed, receding into the darkness. The short man pushed April after him, and they made a single line down the hall. The tall man climbed a staircase at the end of the hall, and in moments Lupita and the rest of the girls emerged on a quiet second-floor landing lined on both sides with closed doors.

Lupita had time to notice about ten doors leading from the hall, each with a deadbolt lock curiously installed backwards with the turning mechanisms facing the hallway. The tall man opened the first door on the left and pushed Lupita inside. When she heard the click in the door behind her, she realized why the locks were backwards. She was trapped.

The room was roughly ten-feet square. In the middle of one wall was a bed with a sagging mattress. The bed slanted slightly toward the foot end, and underneath Lupita could see a book shoved under a broken post.

Smoky light filtered through faded orange curtains. In the corner an aluminum bar holding a single metal hanger was screwed to the wall. In another corner was what appeared to be a closet, but when Lupita looked inside she found a yellowed toilet and a moldy, dripping sink.

The only other furniture in the room was a shiny white bedside table. The top drawer was warped so that one side lay flush in a closed position while the other stuck open like a crooked smile.

Lupita found she was holding the plastic bag with the clothes she had worn yesterday. She was still deciding what to do with it when she heard a loud click and turned to see the bedroom door swing open toward her.

CHAPTER 6

An older man, about her father's age, stepped into the room and closed the door. His command was simple: "Take off your clothes."

Lupita stepped backwards and gasped. "I think you're looking for someone else," she stammered.

The man grinned. "Do you see anyone else here?" he asked, stepping near her.

"No," Lupita choked, "but I don't know you."

"Ah, call me Luis. You owe me quite a lot of money, and you'll have plenty of time to get to know me while you work it off."

"Owe you for what?" Lupita asked boldly, with her back against the wall.

"A plane ticket, for one," the man answered. "Your dress," he motioned, "your passport and visa. I have it all tallied up."

"But I didn't want those things. I didn't agree to come here. I just want to go home," Lupita begged.

"But the fact is, you are here, I purchased you with my own money, and you will begin working here until you can repay me what you owe. Now, I will tell you only once more. Take off your clothes."

Before the house quieted that night, Lupita had been raped three times by three different men. She tried to fight off one of the men after Luis, but that had been a joke. When his fist crashed into her temple, she had passed out. Now, lying in the dark, her body was on fire. She put her hand to her face and felt the plump softness of her swollen eye. And her tears came pouring out.

Upon her arrival in Mexico, Lupita quickly became a hollow husk of a girl. Violated at all times of the day and night, she was occasionally paraded across the compound to the barn she had seen when she arrived. As she had guessed, the barn operated as a cantina, bringing in dozens of men every night.

The twisted routine that Lupita was getting used to involved one of the guards from the house bringing her to the cantina every evening around six o'clock.

The first night she was taken to the cantina, Luis personally took her to a heavy-set man sitting at the far end of the bar. He reminded her of her grandfather.

"Hola, Edward. No coffee this evening?" greeted Luis.

"Sometimes it's better to kick things off with a beer," he laughed, looking Lupita over.

"Well, I know you prefer the Guatemalan blends, so I thought I'd bring you a special gift fresh from the coffee fields."

He pushed Lupita into the man's arms.

"Gracias, Luis. You are always such a gentleman," he said, wrapping an arm around Lupita's waist and pulling her tightly to him.

The bartender brought Edward another beer, and he held it out to Lupita, smiling. "For you," he offered.

Lupita pulled hard away from the man, making him drop the bottle. His smile suddenly dissolved as he stood and picked it up. "Do you know why Luis brought you to me?" he growled, as the smell of beer enveloped them. "It's not only because he knows of my preference for Guatemalans, but because I am especially good at teaching them how to behave." He swept his foot through the puddle on the floor as he added, "And clearly you need some etiquette lessons." He grabbed Lupita savagely by the back of her neck and shoved the beer bottle into her mouth. She choked and coughed, inhaling part of the mouthful as beer ran down the front of her dress. "When someone offers you a drink, you drink it. Understand?"

Around the bar, other men were having what appeared to be similar conversations with the other girls from Lupita's group. At some point each of the new girls was slapped, punched, or otherwise abused. When she caught a glimpse of blood coming from the corner of April's mouth, Lupita was enraged but helpless to do anything.

"So here's your first lesson." Edward turned Lupita's face toward him. "Always remember to smile. Nobody wants a girl who is fighting and angry." He motioned for the bartender to get him another beer. "Now, let's try this again," he said, putting the bottle into her hand. As she tipped it to her lips, Edward smiled. "Much better!" he praised.

As she choked down the beer, Lupita watched three men escort April down a hallway at the back, and instead of beer she felt the silvery electricity of rage fill her stomach.

CHAPTER 7

For two weeks, Lupita went through the evening drill nightly. Her upper body was in a continual throb from the daily beatings she received. Edward was almost exclusively her "teacher." Generally Lupita's evenings began with the beer test until she was semi-convincing at looking like she was having a good time. Usually if she simply pasted a smile on her face she could avoid the worst of Edward's tantrums, but unless she was able to flirt, make small talk, and convincingly perform suggestive touching, she was certain to receive some new bruise or bloodletting.

Without exception, every lesson ended with Lupita practicing her new instructions on mock "clients," who inevitably took her back to her room and performed unspeakable acts she had never before imagined.

One evening as Lupita and her client again walked the steps from the cantina to her room, her thoughts—always distant in times like these—returned to her with a plan. Many times her clients were long past drunk when they made the long walk back to her room. Tonight was such a case. As the man stumbled and plodded behind her, without warning Lupita's thoughts turned to action. As they passed the darkened woodpile she quickly found a bat-sized branch. Turning on the man she now saw as her pursuer, she took advantage of the darkness and brought the club down at an angle between his head and shoulder, directly into his neck. The wobbling man fell like a bag of rice, without so much as a yell or a curse. Before she could even tell how badly she had hurt him, Lupita ran into the desert behind the house.

Within moments she was in the darkness, quickly winded, and lost in a sea of cactus and rocky sand. The brightness from the ever-more distant cantina and a billion shining stars gave her what light she needed as her eyes quickly grew accustomed to the dimness. She tried removing her high heels, but the cruel ground pierced and bruised her feet so mercilessly she had to put them on again.

After nearly an hour stumbling as far away from the cantina as she could get, she still saw its halo of light spreading into the sky above. And the truth began to dawn on her: How far could she possibly go wearing heels and a miniskirt in a god-forsaken wilderness such as this?

The ridiculousness of her situation settled on her by degrees. Perhaps she'd find a road and get a ride with a Good Samaritan. But then she hadn't seen a road in her hour out here. Perhaps she could return to the cantina and make up some story about what happened to her client. But by now the man had been found, and her absence would be conspicuous. What if, once she was caught by Luis's men, she could convince them someone had abducted her? No, the cantina men were evil, not stupid.

So a few minutes later when she saw the headlights of a slow jeep bumping toward her across the desert, she didn't even try to hide.

CHAPTER 8

Darrell lay in the darkness, listening to his wife, Robin, breathing. For two years he'd been working to educate Americans that something insidious was not just in their world or their country, it was in their neighborhoods. His purpose wasn't to help anyone hide from the evil; on the contrary, it was to help them see it.

Having moved to Texas to live in the epicenter of America's sex trade, Darrell knew better than to believe Texas was the only problem area in the United States. And he knew that the United States was just a part of what is a worldwide epidemic in the sale of humans to other humans, a cannibalism of the life and work of the world's most vulnerable people. He also knew the epidemic didn't affect only foreign girls; American girls as young as eleven are also forced into prostitution.

He rolled over and faced the nightstand. The clock glowed 2:54. The images of the previous evening were burned in his mind forever. He and Michael had made a tour of known trafficking locations in Houston. His problem, he knew, was that he couldn't remain emotionally disconnected from the evil he had chosen to reveal, a disconnectedness he'd seen far too many times.

Social atrocities like this always seem to be somebody else's problem. To many people, sex trafficking is a problem in Thailand or in other countries. Unless it hits home personally, human nature tends to kick in, and the busyness of life ends up making it someone else's problem.

Darrell had come to the conclusion that these girls were somebody's children. And he knew, having two beautiful girls of his own, that if anything like this had happened to them he'd want everyone who had the power to stop it to do so. He had to try.

As he traveled throughout the state, speaking at universities, churches, and various places of civic responsibility, every conversation was the same. "How can this be happening?" "That's pretty hard to believe." "I think you're sensationalizing it as a scare tactic." "What can we really do?" He could predict the various responses before he even spoke to a new group. Most were shocked and felt understandably helpless. Like those advocates for worldwide programs to abolish hunger, Darrell knew most people would leave his talks feeling heavy-hearted about the problem. Some would pray for God's hand to intervene, not understanding that they *are* God's hands. Others would work hard to distract themselves with the burdens of their own lives. Some would donate money to help anti-trafficking organizations in the fight. And many would feel so overwhelmed by the magnitude of the problem that they would retreat from its depressing realities. Darrell understood all of the responses; he had personally experienced many of them, and he worked hard not to be judgmental of those who walked away without even trying to understand.

It was the other responses that motivated him to press on. Like that one great golf shot that kept him playing the game, it was those one or two people—and for some groups, several people—who would step to the plate and, with bold determination and a sense of purpose, join the fight.

At its root, Darrell understood that the heart of modern-day slavery is self-centeredness, and that victims are trapped between lust and greed. He could trace in the men and women who were lost in the modern culture of sexual addiction the path leading from fulfillment of their selfish desires to their current place—fueling the demand for trafficked victims. And because of their willingness to buy another person to gratify their selfish lust, an entrepreneur would be more than happy to sell one to gratify his greed. Lust and greed, the bookends that hold the stories of thousands of beautiful children whose hopes and dreams have been sold for a buck.

But it wasn't just the commercial sex trade that infuriated him. He knew of case after case where otherwise upstanding men and women in America had housekeepers who they treated every bit as terribly as America's slaves were treated before the Civil War. His stomach turned at the thought of the children's choir from Sudan that had made a tour through American's churches, where unsuspecting congregants who housed the children had no idea their donations went into the pocket of the choir director who had abducted the boys and girls.

Dear God, protect my girls and help Robin and me be the kind of parents who will create an environment of hope and stability for them. Lord, we are very aware that even with that, they are at risk in a society of greed and lust. I pray, Lord, that they would have a Christ-centered community in their lives that would rally around them and love them. I pray that you would protect them from the influences and peer pressures that bombard them. O God, my girls represent to me the thousands of children who are not asleep in their own beds tonight but instead are servicing men in the devil's bedrooms scattered across our cities and around our world—their comfort, safety, and childhood stolen from them to feed the lusts and greed of our society. Darrell continued to pray on into the night as the faces of real girls like Maria flooded his mind.

CHAPTER 9

On the evening of her attempted escape Lupita began to understand how those who perform torture can believe they are artists. She had been beaten by a silent man who was talented at making women feel pain. He hadn't tortured Lupita for information. He hadn't done it for any purpose other than to discipline her. Surely she had paid for her ill-conceived escape attempt.

Still bound to the bed, lying twisted like a corpse, Lupita listened to the man leave. As he clicked off the light, she could barely see the darkness through her swollen, coin-slot eyes.

In and out of consciousness, she had no way of telling how much time passed except to note the brightness filling the room through the window and that the blood in her nose and mouth had dried. She much preferred unconsciousness to being awake, for her waking moments were accompanied by searing pain in every pore of her body.

At some point she heard the bedroom door open, heavy boots scuff across the floor, and the click as her shackles were removed. Strong arms lifted her roughly and carried her out the door and down the stairs.

When consciousness returned, she found herself lying on her back on a hard surface in complete darkness. She tried to touch her face, and felt a hundred needles stab every inch of flesh that moved. Foolishly she tried to raise her other arm, only to experience the same excruciating result. Flex her thigh? Same result. Turn her ankle? Same. She didn't have to wonder what sort of predicament she was in for long. Soon a door opened, and footsteps came near her. She waited, expecting some new torture. Instead she simply heard the breathing of someone standing near her . . . doing what?

"Ah my angel," came Luis's soft voice. Just the sound of it made Lupita's stomach jolt violently. "I thought the older girl would be the one we had to make an example of," he said. "Hugo said it would be you, but I told him you were far too smart to try to escape. That Hugo is a perceptive one," he sighed.

A strong light suddenly snapped on. After a few moments her eyes adjusted to the brightness, and she realized they were in a basement-like room. She lay near a concrete wall with fluorescent workshop lights above. She almost chuckled when she realized how inventive her torturers had been; the needles that pierced her with every flexed muscle were a wrap of barbed wire, tightly surrounding her bed from her neck to the bottoms of her feet.

Luis continued, "I must apologize, but for your safety I feel compelled to keep you confined in your present posture for a bit. No doubt if I let you go back to your normal routine now, we'd just find you swinging from the light fixture in your room by evening. Trust me, I know this from experience. I'll be back in the morning to check on you again. Until then, I'll let you rest."

At some point much later, Lupita awoke to the opening of the basement door and the blaze of lights in her eyes. She found her eyes opened more widely than they had last time she tried, although the pain in her body was ever-present. The man who had abused her in her room after her escape attempt approached the bed and began unwrapping the wire. As he unwrapped her, the door opened again and Luis walked in.

Lupita raised her hand to her face, and the joint in her elbow creaked painfully. She tried sitting, and the rush of blood from her head made her lie back down immediately.

"There's no rush," Luis advised. "We are not quite done here yet."

CHAPTER 10

When Lupita finally managed to sit up without the dizziness, she found her head throbbing in time to the pain of her other injuries. Her joints blazed like fire from the stiffness.

"*Mi chica tierna,*" Luis soothed, as he held out his hand. Lupita eyed his hand suspiciously until Luis helped her up.

"You've had a hard night. How about some finer furniture?" He guided her to a large leather recliner that faced an entertainment center. "I have some things I need to show you. See, had we let you go yesterday, you would no doubt have sought the quickest way out of the consequences for your poor choices, and I do not like to have to deal with corpses. Also, you have a special part of my heart, and I just couldn't let that happen to you. However, I would be a fool to think that a single night to think over your foolish ideas is enough to make you forget such rash decisions. So before you return to your room, you will want to see this."

Luis placed a DVD with a handwritten label into the player and started it. The scene that unfolded appeared to have been recorded on a handheld video camera inside a police station. Lupita saw the men from the airport talking to uniformed officers.

Luis began to narrate. "This is our local police station. Every now and then one of our girls believes she can run out on her debts to us and tries to flee just as you have done."

Lupita watched on the video as an officer brought out a filthy woman dressed in a low-cut blouse and miniskirt. The officer let go of the woman, but she did not move. Finally he pushed her into the arms of the waiting men.

"The officials here understand that we all owe debts to someone. Like me, they do what they can to make sure everyone pays up. The woman you see here was picked up by the police within hours of fleeing our ranch. This video wasn't filmed until three days later when they decided to tell us they'd found her. If you believe these last few hours were unpleasant for you, you should be glad your experience was better than that of this woman. See, prostitution is illegal. And to these men, she was nothing more than a common hooker. So besides being considered a criminal in the eyes of the Mexican government, she has had a very bad experience in this jail. The police are not friends of women such as you."

Luis clicked off the DVD player and sat in a chair opposite Lupita. "I imagine you see the wisdom of staying here where we feed you and give you a warm place to sleep in exchange for your work. But in case you don't, I have one final incentive to convince you to stay."

From his jacket pocket Luis pulled a glossy photograph and handed it to Lupita. The picture was taken at her family's stall in the Plaza Mayor. She almost cried when she saw her little sister, Natalia, working the stall. In the photo Natalia was holding out a plastic bag in which she had placed the fruit a customer had just purchased. Lupita gasped when she saw to whom Natalia was handing the fruit—the same man who had tortured her!

Luis saw the look of horror on Lupita's face. "I do not like this part of my job. But some girls are just so stubborn that despite all the dangers of our countryside and our police force, they still insist on leaving us. And in the unlikely event that they disappear without a trace, I must have a way to recoup my investment. In such a case, I have options. We know where your family lives, and we know you are very close to your sister. If you decide to leave us before your debt is paid, we will have no other option than to pay her a visit. She may be lucky; we may have room for her here. Of course, your debt will be added to the cost of her expenses as well. But we do not always have room for more workers here. In such times as that, we still must honor our word to you. If this event should come to pass, I can only hope that your sister's death will be quick and painless. But I fear that Raoul is not always the most efficient person at his job."

CHAPTER 11

Within forty-eight hours of her escape attempt, Lupita was back at work in the cantina, a model employee for Luis's enterprise. He was clearly pleased with her behavior, as she pretended to enjoy her time with her clients and flirted relentlessly even with the men who were not her own clients.

Thirty-six hours later a Caucasian man drove onto the ranch in a brand new Ford truck. He parked by the cantina and let himself in. A half-hour later Luis and the man emerged from the cantina and made their way to the house. Lupita was not aware of any of this until Luis opened the door to her room. He stuck his head in and said simply, "Get your things and meet me downstairs. You've graduated." She arrived downstairs before Luis returned. A strange man sat comfortably on the couch smoking a cigar and eyeing Lupita.

"Mornin' sunshine," he chirped cheerfully. Lupita painted on the smile she had been taught to use and returned his greeting. To her surprise she saw he held two of the plastic bags of travel documents that she had first seen at Señora Ramirez's house. After a few short moments Luis returned with April in tow.

"Ladies," Luis announced, "this is Clint. I am pleased to say you've both made fine progress in learning the entertainment trade here, and he is going to take charge of the next stage of your education." He stepped close to Lupita. "It's a shame you'll have to be moving on," he said quietly. "I have so enjoyed our time together." He took each of the girls' hands and kissed them in his best Prince Charming impersonation. "But now I must bid you goodbye."

"Ha!" laughed Clint, "You're a regular Casanova." He moved to the front door and held it open. "Ladies," he said, motioning for them to step outside.

As they got in the truck, Clint asked casually, "So, either of you ever been to Juárez?"

CHAPTER 12

Clint was a talker, the kind of person who can't manage a real conversation because he's always thinking of his next words. Not that there were any voices other than his in the truck anyway. But he didn't seem to notice.

"Luis says y'all are from Central America, huh? Never been south of the border myself. Don't even like to come south of the U.S. of A. Ain't it pretty much the same as Mexico? I'm from Lousiana, but I hang my hat in Texas and call that home."

Lupita, sitting by the window with April sandwiched between her and Clint, simply stared at the passing landscape. She tried to think about how she might escape. But every time she began to raise her hopes, she remembered Luis holding the picture of Natalia and realized that any complete escape plan had to include returning home and rescuing Natalia too. Several hours later April crawled into the back-seat of the truck and went to sleep. Lupita was afraid to fall asleep, afraid of the unknown that might happen when her eyes were closed. But her attempts to stay awake were no match for the monotony of the road and soon she, too, had fallen asleep.

When Lupita awoke it was because of the stop-and-go motion of the truck. They were in a brightly lit area, and as she was rubbing the sleep from her eyes, she saw a billboard that read "border parking." She sat up, wondering where they were. Just off the highway sat what looked like a restaurant. In front of the truck sat hundreds of cars in a line pointed toward a bridge. The cars and trucks were passing through what appeared to be drive-through offices right on the bridge.

"You woke up just in time, young lady. Just about to cross the border," said Clint.

After a lengthy time of sitting in traffic, Clint finally pulled up beside a border agent. "Good evening," greeted the woman.

"Evening, ma'am," said Clint sweetly. He and the agent exchanged conversation, with Clint providing the girls' documents along with his own. The agent shined her flashlight into the truck, looking Lupita and April in the face, and then looking at the documents Clint had given her.

"Have a good evening," the woman replied abruptly, standing up straight and looking back to the next car in line.

Clint drove on into a blessedly open stretch of road, and Lupita noticed how quickly the signs changed—Harley Davidson, McDonald's, Motel 6. He was clearly familiar with the area, soon exiting the highway and driving local streets until he came to a motel.

After he'd checked in, Clint led the girls to adjoining rooms around the rear of the building. Lupita had only a few moments to wonder whether she and April would have to sleep in the same room as him when he handed her a key and stopped in front of a pair of rooms.

"That one's yours," he said, putting the key into the doorknob of one of the rooms. "Go open the door that connects it to this one."

Lupita let herself and April into the room, and when she opened the door connecting the rooms, Clint was standing there waiting.

"Keep this door open at all times," he directed as he stepped into the girls' room. "Call me old-fashioned, but I think women need their own place." He then went to the door that led outside and flipped closed the safety bar, attaching a combination padlock to it. "Relax and clean up. Tomorrow we'll do a little shopping. I don't like to get up early, so don't turn on your television until I'am awake."

In their own room, the girls sat on the bed and stared at each other. For the first time, Lupita felt she was really seeing April, about the same age as Natalia. Though she was only fifteen years old herself, Lupita looked at April and saw an elementary girl scared beyond the edge of reason, terrified into becoming a different person entirely. As the girls looked at each other, for the first time alone together and without the fear of who or what was coming through the door, they both began to weep. Lupita put her arms around April, and they cried quietly, longer than either girl could ever remember having cried before.

As they sat together, Lupita began to put together a mental list of things to do to make life feel normal again. Bathe, television, story, and bedtime. Clint had said they would go shopping tomorrow; she wondered what kind of shopping.

Lupita ran a warm bath, then helped April undress. She cringed as she saw the wounds on April's body, wounds completely hidden by the clothing she had been given, wounds inflicted with a knowledge of exactly where to hurt a little girl without it being visible to casual observers. In Lupita's mind, April was not just a girl the same age as Natalia, she *was* Natalia, a child to be protected and cherished.

"Do you want me to leave the door open?" Lupita asked as April stepped into the bath.

April nodded. "Will you stay here with me?"

"Of course," Lupita smiled, knowing that being alone now seemed a worse fate than anything that had happened in the last few days.

Later the girls sat in bed together as Lupita told stories of her family and their stall in Plaza Mayor. And when a stab of memory pierced her heart upon remembering that her own uncle had sold her into this life, she pushed it as far down inside as she could, pretending she still didn't know how she got here.

The next morning Lupita and April had been awake for hours when they finally heard Clint stirring in his room. The sun was already high, and both girls were famished when Clint strolled into their room and opened the padlock.

"Phew," Clint said, sniffing at the girls. The sooner we get those clothes changed the better. Lupita was aware that no matter how clean she was, her filthy clothing made her always seem to need a bath. The thought of new clothes was as delicious as Christmas.

An hour later the girls walked out of a department store with two bags apiece, and each girl wore a new outfit. Clint took the bags that held their old clothes and stuffed them in a trashcan as they left. Smiling, he asked, "How about some grub?" Not that it mattered, but both girls couldn't nod their approval quickly enough.

After an amazing lunch where Clint seemed eager to stuff the girls full of food, he drove the back streets to an old warehouse where two semitrucks sat parked at a loading dock. He disappeared into the warehouse for a few minutes, then returned.

"We got ourselves a new ride," he proclaimed. "Let's go." The girls did as they were told, leaving the pickup and loading into the semi. A short time later Clint turned back out onto the interstate in their new ride. Neither girl asked where they were headed, but both wondered what events the next stop held.

CHAPTER 13

"It's Economics 101," Darrell began, trying to make the issue as simple and clear as possible for the men's group he was addressing. "It's the law of supply and demand. In this case the supply is driven by the demand. Let me explain. If no one is buying twelve-year-old girls—*demand*, no one will be selling twelve-year-old girls—*supply*. Pimps and traffickers are businessmen. They only sell what people are buying." Darrell's passion began to show as his voice elevated and his animation increased.

"I need a volunteer," he said.

Pointing to a forty-two-year-old businessman, he continued, "You, sir."

As the man approached the stage Darrell asked, "And what is your name?"

"John," the man answered.

"Perfect!" Darrell laughed and then continued to question him, discovering he met all the qualifications to be the average john in America: middle-aged businessman with a wife, a couple of kids, and living in the suburbs.

"The average man who sleeps with twelve-year-old trafficking victims," Darrell announced with passion, "is not who you might think he is. He isn't wearing a stained wife-beater T-shirt with a beer gut hanging out. Nor does he look like the typical pervert of the big screen. Any one of you in this room could qualify. By the way, that's why those who pay to have sex with minors are called 'john'—they look like normal, average, everyday American men."

Darrell tackles his work with passion. He speaks regularly to men's groups, churches, colleges and universities, women's teas—to just about anyone who will give him the time of day.

Darrell's position was created because of a federal grant given to the Houston Rescue and Restore Coalition. The coalition is in charge of five different organizations that are each responsible for one aspect in the anti-trafficking fight. Darrell's work is to help end the demand for trafficked victims.

As he began his work, Darrell quickly realized three distinct elements that make sex trafficking work. On one end is the pimp/trafficker who actively markets his product, and on the other end is the buyer of the pimp's product—the "john." Caught in the middle is the "product," a sad term given to real people, the victims of the john's lust and the pimp's greed.

In his seminar called "Pimping America," Darrell unfolds the sickening reality of a culture that feeds the problem.

"We live in a culture that glamorizes the pimp, normalizes the john, and dehumanizes the victim," Darrell proclaimed from one pulpit. "'Yo, yo, pimp my . . .'" he started, then motioned for the congregation to finish his sentence.

"Ride!" the crowd yelled as Darrell paused.

"Exactly. To 'pimp' has come to mean 'to improve upon.' And we glamorize him and what he has and fail to look at how he got his bling.

"And john, well he is just the everyday, normal American. But then look at what we call the victim."

Darrell's voice changed, and there was an overwhelming sense of sadness as he slowly said, "Slut . . . whore . . . ho . . . lot lizards at the truck stops . . . even prostitute." A hush came over the congregation as their understanding of the culture they live in began to move beyond their limited knowledge of MTV and media exposure. At times Darrell wonders if this hush among the Christian community is because they are truly processing these realities or because they are offended at the profaneness they acknowledge in their worlds.

Darrell knows as well as anyone that government control is not going to solve the problem in America. Because of this truth, his goal is to help engage people in identifying and implementing solutions. And he also knows there is no other single entity as well-suited to this purpose than God's church.

It is Darrell's dream that the people of God become leaders in the rescue and restoration of sex-trafficking victims and the prevention of sex trafficking altogether. He fantasizes that in their repulsion Christians would not retreat to their ivory tower, but instead advance as a united army fighting the good fight for justice, setting the captives free.

CHAPTER 14

As Clint pulled the truck into a truck stop east of El Paso, he announced, "Say hello to your place of business, ladies. But first, a little education."

In a corner of the truck stop restaurant, Clint taught the girls about the new form their lives would take. "About nine o'clock tonight this lot is going to fill up with tired drivers looking to relax. Inside each of these trucks are men from all walks of life, but they all have a few things in common—long days and lonely nights. You'll see some here connecting with their families by video chatting. Others will hang out in the lounge just shooting the bull. But you're here for a different crowd. You're here to connect with the drivers who are looking for a good time." Clint droned on for another half-hour about life at the truck stop and how Lupita and April would earn money from the truckers. He spent a considerable amount of time talking about how to avoid the police who made a frequent routine of visiting the stations. "Keep in mind that prostitution is illegal," Clint warned.

Prostitution? Lupita was shocked at the recognition of the word. It was the first time she'd heard the word since Luis had mentioned it, and it hit her like a bag of rocks. She wasn't a prostitute! Prostitutes choose their jobs. There was no choice involved in her being here. But even as she argued with herself about the hundred good reasons she should not be considered a prostitute, she knew that anyone—*anyone*—would consider her a prostitute nevertheless.

Back in the truck, after a lesson on using the CB to find customers, darkness had fallen. The dashboard clock read 7:45. "You ma'am," Clint pointed at Lupita, "will go by the name 'Latin Love.' And before we go home tonight, I need each of you to bring in five hundred dollars."

Each girl took her turn using the CB, trying to sound sexy and alluring to the drivers who were headed their way. Clint coached them on what to say, and finally he fell silent as they understood exactly what he expected.

"Hey guys," said Lupita seductively into the CB, "this is Latin Love. Anyone at this truck stop looking for some company tonight?"

A voice immediately responded, "Latin Love, this is Slim Jim, comeback."

"Hey Slim Jim, how was the drive in?"

"Long and hard, and I *am* looking to relax."

"Oh, that's too bad. I was hoping party row was hoppin' tonight. I'm looking for a dance."

"Well, by the looks of the row," said Slim Jim, "you might be in luck."

"So Slim Jim, which rig is yours?" Lupita asked in her sexiest voice.

"I'm in a white Kenworth with the curtains pulled, near the exit," he answered. "Hope to see you soon; let's dance."

Lupita pasted on the smile she had been trained to use and slipped from the cab of the truck. She saw Clint hand the CB to April.

Lupita began to walk down party row looking for Slim Jim's truck. She found it only four rigs down and across from where Clint had strategically parked their Mack. Clint watched as Lupita straightened her skirt and adjusted her blouse before reaching up and knocking on the white door. As the door opened he watched her high heels disappear into the rig, then turned his attention back to April who was still looking for a date on the CB.

Nine minutes after Lupita had entered Slim Jim's rig, she thanked him and slipped the sixty dollars he had given her into her small red purse that matched her red heels. He thanked her for a good time and said he hoped to see her again down the road. Lupita opened the passenger door, slipped down, and walked toward the front of the rig. When she reached the front she glanced toward Clint, knowing he would be watching for her. She began walking down party row looking for her next date. His eye picked her up as she turned her back toward him and approached the next truck in line. *Sixty dollars down, another $440 to go*, she thought.

CHAPTER 15

Four hours and seven men later, Lupita had earned her evening's quota. April had not done so well, earning only $325. In the past two hours Clint had gotten more and more hostile, first cursing then screaming at April when she'd return to the truck. The last time she returned, Clint got out to let April in only to give her a vicious shove just as she was about to step into the truck.

He stormed in behind her and jammed the truck into gear. They made their way back to El Paso in silence, returning to the warehouse to change vehicles, and then back to the previous night's motel. As Clint put the lock on the girls' door and moved back to his room, he seized April by the back of the neck and dragged her into his room. The only coherent thing Lupita heard Clint scream was, "I said five hundred dollars!"

She couldn't bear April's screams she heard as Clint raped her and then burned the bottom of her feet and back of her neck with his cigarette. She covered her ears and buried her head in her pillow, crying in rhythm with April's sobs.

When Clint pushed April back into her room, the only thing he had to say was, "You've got a lot of debt to pay off, little lady. You better consider how you're going to do a better job tomorrow."

The next evening the routine was the same. Clint acted as if last night's events had never happened, even presenting a gift to each of the girls. "Just a little something to perk you up," he said, smiling. "And though I hate to mention it, I had to add the cost of those to your tab." Inside each package was a silver necklace with a string of three pearls. It would have seemed beautiful to Lupita had it not been for the knowledge of what the gift was going to cost her.

Back at the truck stop, as big rigs began pulling in for the night, Clint handed the CB to April. "Here you go, princess. Make yourself convincing."

"Horizontal Highway Hostess at your service. Anybody hungry?" April announced. Lupita raised her eyebrows in surprise, but April didn't notice. She was focused on making sure she didn't have to relive Clint's wrath tonight. Within minutes she was in a conversation with a client. Lupita wondered if the man on the other end of the CB would even care if he knew April was a twelve-year-old girl.

As April climbed out of the cab to meet her first client, Lupita followed behind her. "Careful little sister," she called, then added, "I love you."

Lupita headed for the nearest line of trucks and stopped at the first one she came to. She knocked on the door. The window opened only a crack.

"Looking for a date?" she asked in a sultry voice.

"Not tonight, honey" he answered.

"I'll bet you're tired. Need a massage?"

"No, sorry, not interested."

Lupita grabbed the mirror with her left hand and pulled herself up onto the running board where he could see her better. Adjusting her blouse with her right hand to reveal more of her cleavage, she continued, "I have the best hands on the lot, perfect for relieving the stress of the strongest trucker out here. Sixty dollars gets you fifteen minutes of relief."

"I said I'm not interested. Now go away and don't come back. And tell your other sleazy little lizard friends to stay away as well."

Knowing it would not be a sale, and that she didn't have time to waste, Lupita continued on. She moved around the truck to the next and knew it, too, would be a waste of time as her eye caught the degrading and humiliating sticker in the lower corner of the driver's window. The sticker was a lizard dressed in a miniskirt and heels and wearing bright red lipstick. It was in the center of a red circle with a wide red diagonal line through the middle. It was a clear message that "lot lizards" were not welcome at this truck. For Lupita it was also a reminder that the more of those she saw, the more chance there was she wouldn't make her quota. Receiving her own lesson from Clint was not high on her list of things she wanted to do.

Glancing back over her left shoulder she saw April slipping out of a blue rig across and down from her. This meant one less trick for Lupita, but she was glad for April.

By 1:30 A.M. each girl handed Clint five hundred dollars.

"Well, well, well. Nicely done, ladies!" he congratulated. "Climb in back there and make yourselves comfortable. We're moving on tonight."

Lupita and April lay down in the sleeper cab. When Lupita heard April's sobs, she moved nearer and put her arm around the girl. But April pushed her away, scooting further toward the edge of the bed. Whether her tears came from some new violation or the pain of the accumulated days, Lupita didn't know. There was so much to cry about.

CHAPTER 16

For the next week Clint continued driving east along I-10. At the end of their last day on the road, Clint pulled the truck into another warehouse, this time in Houston.

"Get your things. We're going to be here a while," Clint advised. He grabbed the girls' plastic bags of travel documents from under the seat and climbed out of the truck.

The three went through the door beside the loading dock. Immediately inside the warehouse was a woman working on a computer at a desk. Clint exchanged waves with her as he led the girls across the open expanse of the warehouse and into a sparsely furnished office area.

"Whatcha know, Rick?" Clint greeted a middle-aged Caucasian man in the offices.

"Nothing new under the sun, my friend," the man replied.

"You ladies can sit here a bit," Clint motioned to a row of hard-backed chairs. There was a television set suspended on a platform near the ceiling that was tuned to a sports channel. Below it sat a water cooler with paper cups. "You're going to be waiting here with Rick for a while. Our truck stop learnin' is done for the time being, and this man will prep you for your new homes."

With that, Clint returned from the direction they had come, and like Señora Ramirez, it was the last they ever saw of him.

After the girls had waited in silence for several more hours an older woman came into the office. She looked at the girls closely, then sat down at Rick's desk. Lupita couldn't quite hear everything they were saying, but she was sure the two were talking about her and April. She tried not to stare but continued to glance out of the corner of her eye. At one point she was sure she saw the woman place their travel documents into her purse.

After more long moments the woman approached Lupita and April.

"Hola, ladies," she greeted, "I am Señora Esteban. Come along now. I'll take you to your new home."

Back outside, the three entered a large red sedan, and before long they were on the road again, heading through the streets of Houston.

Not far past Houston's downtown, they exited the freeway and made their way through an industrial area alongside some train tracks. They arrived at what was either a small warehouse or a large house. A dirt parking lot big enough to hold half a dozen cars sat empty in front of the building. A large door and small cement porch looked out on the world that passed by. Señora Esteban led April and Lupita to the front door, produced a key, and guided them inside.

Inside the door was a landing that welcomed visitors to use the stairs leading upward. A large man in a padded chair sat back by the door and eyed them intently as they entered.

"Hola, Enrique," said Señora Esteban. "New residents for you."

Enrique silently nodded to the three as they headed up the stairs. One flight up Lupita suddenly stopped, a deer caught in the glare of oncoming headlights. The landing at the second floor looked alarmingly similar to the second floor of the cantina where she'd been kept not so long ago.

Another floor up, Señora Esteban led the girls halfway down the hall, stopping at the third door on the left. She produced another key on a temporary cardboard key ring and opened the door. Lupita gasped at what she saw.

"Are we supposed to stay here?" Lupita asked.

"Is there something wrong with it?" asked Señora Esteban.

"Oh no, it's very nice," said Lupita. And she meant it. Rather than the single bare room she'd expected, she stood in a shabbily furnished studio apartment. An old couch, recliner, coffee table, and television set hugged the room's walls. To her left, through a cutout in the wall, she could see a small kitchen.

Señora Esteban looked down at the bags the girls carried and said, "Well, doesn't look like you need a lot of storage space, which is good." She led the two into another room and flipped on the light in a small bedroom. A twin bed and nightstand were the only furnishings. A closet with mirrored sliding doors flanked the entry door.

"There are a few groceries in the kitchen. They've been added to what you owe. And you'll have to start making plans to supply your own. You'll want to eat dinner before six o'clock tonight. Someone will be back by then to pick you up." At that, Señora Esteban turned and left the apartment, setting the key on the kitchen table as she left.

Both girls simply stood and looked at each other, trying to understand exactly what had just happened. This was their new home? Given the events of the past days, neither girl protested. It was practically a palace compared to every place they'd been since Señora Ramirez's.

"What do you think happens at six?" asked April?

CHAPTER 17

The next few weeks dragged by like snails on a summer holiday. The first evening they arrived in Houston, Lupita and April were taken to the cantina. Upon seeing her new place of employment, Lupita died a little more. The reality of her new world was complete. When she saw that the owner of the cantina was Enrique—the same man who sat in the entry to her apartment—she realized he wasn't there to protect her, but rather to keep her from leaving.

It took barely an hour to learn the ropes at the new place. The routine was similar to the cantina where they'd been trained: get a man to buy you a drink, and he could touch you however he wanted until your drink was gone. If he wanted more than a drinking companion, there was a house behind the bar where there was privacy. Work seven days a week, 365 days a year, and pretend you are making headway in paying back an impossible debt.

On a typical evening Lupita entertained fifteen or twenty men. The only way she could cope with her routine was to take her mind somewhere separate from the physical location of her tête-à-têtes. She was never tempted to like any man she met in her work, but she appreciated those who were gentle. It was not infrequent that men asked her why she was in this line of work. While they perpetuated the injustice being done to countless girls, they also seemed to sense their guilt and wanted to rescue her.

Of the thirty girls who worked at the cantina, Lupita knew only a handful. Besides April, the only one she could consider a friend was Maria. Lupita had no idea how long Maria had been at the cantina, but she also lived in the apartment next to theirs. Sometimes during the day April and Lupita visisted Maria in her apartment and watched television. Maria became like a mentor to the two girls, helping them avoid the violence of Enrique or his men, and giving them ideas on how to work through the clients as quickly as possible.

Maria, too, had been taken from her home in Central America and traveled much the same path to the cantina as Lupita and April. It felt good to Lupita to have someone else who understood what she and April had gone through and was still surviving.

The first lesson Maria taught the girls was to keep their friendship a secret. "If it looks like we're too close, Enrique will move you to a different place. He doesn't like his girls getting to know each other. It increases the chance we'll all gang up on him or escape together or something."

"What about us?" April asked, referring to her obvious friendship with Lupita.

"You came as a pair, so I wouldn't worry about it. But it wouldn't hurt to pretend that you don't like each other very much!"

CHAPTER 18

Occasionally a few girls from the apartment were driven to a grocery store to shop. Lupita was rarely allowed to roam freely, and any time such a thing happened, Enrique was there to remind her he knew where her sister was, and that Natalia would pay for any poor choices Lupita might make.

April was more difficult for Enrique to coerce because she had no younger siblings. For a while he threatened her with the possibility of harming her parents, but soon she gave up caring. So on her thirteenth birthday he arrived at the apartment around lunchtime. He was carrying an armful of cardboard Chinese food containers and some presents.

"Hey birthday girl," he cheered when April saw him. "Brought you some gifts to make your day special." He served April and Lupita the Chinese food, then gave April two gifts—a fancy makeup kit and a small leather purse. When she opened the purse, April found what she thought were marijuana cigarettes. She looked at Enrique in surprise.

"And that's the real surprise, sweetie pie," Enrique said cheerfully. He took out a single cigarette and lit it. He took a puff, then handed it to April.

"No thank you," April said sheepishly.

"Now baby girl, don't think you can just pass on a gift. I got those especially for you. You'd be hurting my feelings if you passed them up."

April took a hesitant puff, then looked at Lupita. Lupita knew if Enrique told her to smoke too, she'd have to do it. But he didn't, and it was a good thing. Fifteen minutes later April was euphoric. Lupita wasn't a drug user, but she had seen plenty of it in the Plaza Mayor back home, and she was sure that whatever April was experiencing wasn't marijuana. After a while April lay down on the couch smiling, and began to drift asleep.

"Feels good, huh, baby girl?" Enrique asked.

"Oh, yeah," mumbled April.

Enrique put her new purse next to the couch. "Well, if you need more, it's right here. And one more birthday surprise . . . no need to come to work. Just stay right here and enjoy yourself until tomorrow."

Lupita had planned to take away the drugs as soon as Enrique left, but he seemed to know what she was thinking.

"Get your things," he said to Lupita. "Let's let her enjoy herself alone."

After a long night of working, Lupita returned home early the next morning to the smell of vomit and an unconscious roommate. She peeked into April's new purse and noticed without surprise that it was empty.

"Come on, sis, let's get you to bed," said Lupita, half carrying and half dragging the girl from the living room to the bedroom. Had she thought about it very long it would not have been difficult to realize this would become a routine.

When it finally dawned on Lupita several days later that Enrique had intentionally gotten April addicted to heroin, it seemed so obvious that she chastised herself for not realizing it sooner. As dependent as she was on the drugs only Enrique could provide, April didn't even require guards at the doors. Enrique couldn't have gotten rid of her if he wanted to.

CHAPTER 19

For the next two months April existed in a near constant stupor. Any time Enrique needed to exercise his will over her, it took only the merest mention of withholding the drug to convince her to obey.

One early morning in May, when the dark air was still crisp, the two girls arrived in their apartment together as was their usual custom. They had barely stepped in the door when April produced a clear plastic bag of her drug. Lupita knew from the large quantity that Enrique would never have given her that much.

"Where'd you get that?" Lupita asked April.

April laughed in what had become her standard slurred speech. "Remember the creepy guy with the pierced cheek? Turns out he's a dealer!" she laughed hysterically.

"He didn't give that to you, did he?"

"Let's just say I'm borrowing it," April giggled.

Lupita double-checked the front door to make sure it was locked. If that guy was anything like Enrique, she knew when he discovered his missing drugs he was going to figure out where they went. And the result wouldn't be pretty.

It didn't take long. The next night Lupita wasn't even in the bar when he came in, and when she heard shots from the room down the hall in the building behind the cantina, it didn't even occur to her that April was the cause. A brief silence followed the shots, but when she heard screaming she told her john, "You better get out of here fast!" But he was already halfway out the door.

The last time Lupita saw April, she was just a bump under a blanket being pushed into the back of an ambulance.

Lupita went home that night and mourned April silently. She sat for hours remembering everything they'd gone through. And no matter how she tried to wrap her mind around what life would be like without her, she just couldn't do it. There was no going on without April. By the time the sun rose, Lupita was searching the apartment for every type of medication she could find. She reasoned that if she could put enough medicine into her body, she too would go to sleep and never wake up. And that's nearly what happened.

When she woke up, before she'd even opened her eyes, she knew she was in a strange place. The quiet hum of machines surrounded her, and someone nearby seemed to be turning pages in a magazine. She had no recollection of where she was or how she'd gotten there. She lay still, trying to remember anything. The first image that came to mind was April being shoved into the ambulance, and at once her memory opened again, and she began to cry.

A soft hand grabbed hers, and a woman's voice soothed, "It's okay, honey. It's okay. You're safe now."

Lupita opened her eyes and saw Maria standing beside her bed. Lupita held her hand and wept harder than she had since the first night after the truck stop.

"How did I get here, Maria? How did I get here? This isn't how life is supposed to go!" she cried.

"I know, baby. Trust me, I know. But we're free now."

Lupita looked both startled and terrified. "What do you mean free?"

An FBI agent stepped up to the bedside next to Maria. "This is a police officer," Maria said, motioning to the plainly dressed man.

Lupita screamed in fear as she clung desperately to Maria. "Get him out of here! Just get him out!" Since Mexico, the fear of the police had been bred into her. She'd heard hundreds of stories of the police at the truck stops, at the massage parlors, and at the cantinas. She'd serviced policemen at the bar. She knew they were not to be trusted, and they held the power of prisons and immigration and courts.

After a great while Maria managed to calm Lupita once more. "It's okay. He's been here since last night when you came in. I've talked to him for a long time. He's okay. You need to talk to him. He can help us."

When Lupita was too tired to fight anymore, Maria dismissed herself. "I'll be right outside the door where you can see me. If you need me, just call, okay? You'll be safe."

The agent explained that Lupita had overdosed on medication, the memory of which was beginning to come back to her even without his help. Apparently Maria had discovered her unconscious in the apartment and called Enrique. He then put her unconscious body into the trunk of Señora Esteban's car, but not without arousing the suspicions of a driver in a passing vehicle. The driver called 911 from his cell phone, and the police intercepted Enrique at the docks as he was preparing to dump Lupita into the water.

The agent explained he was with the FBI and had been studying the cantina for a long time. The FBI suspected it was an endpoint for trafficked victims who had been abducted and transported via a crime syndicate in Mexico. With the sudden arrest of Enrique, and subsequently the remaining workers at the cantina, the police were desperate to get enough evidence to convict them on trafficking charges. "But," the agent explained, "we need you to help us."

At this last request, Lupita shut down. She was no longer interested in hearing the man now that she knew what he wanted. When the agent detected her unresponsiveness, he excused himself and left the room.

Before long Maria returned, along with two other men. She introduced them as Michael and Darrell, and said they were her friends.

"We don't have friends," Lupita chuckled. Then she added, "Haven't I seen you at the cantina before?"

Maria explained how she'd enjoyed getting to know Michael and how—despite the fact that he visited the cantina—she realized he was not a john but was instead someone who could help answer their questions.

"It's a pleasure to meet you," one of the men said.

Maria spent the next hour talking and arguing with Lupita about cooperating with the police. Lupita was terrified of Enrique and all the other people she had met on her trip from Guatemala to Houston. Though Enrique was in jail, she had no confidence he'd stay there. And most of the demons she'd met were still out there somewhere. She feared for herself and Natalia if she cooperated with the police.

"Look, sister," Maria reasoned, "do you know why we've been held in that bar for so long? Because the police couldn't prove we were being held against our will. If they'd come straight up to me and asked, 'Hey, are you a slave?' I'd have guaranteed I was there by my own choosing. And you would have too."

Lupita started to protest, but Maria cut her off.

"Don't you go arguing with me," she commanded. "You would have denied it to any official-type person. I mean look, you nearly pulled my hair out when I simply told you that guy was a cop. Don't try making me think you'd have spilled your guts to some complete stranger, not to mention the fact that Enrique was always listening to what we were saying to people anyway."

"You're right," Lupita conceded. "But won't we get in trouble for being prostitutes?"

"Girl, we're no prostitutes! We're slaves! Just because we take money for sex doesn't mean we're volunteering to do it. When the alternative is getting beat within an inch of your life, or sent walking back to Central America, or your family being murdered or brought into this same hell, man, that ain't no volunteer work.

"So here's the deal," she continued, "if you join me and a couple of the other girls in telling the police the truth about what life has been like for us, there's no way they're going to let Enrique just up and walk out of there. He'll be serving life by the time he gets out of court. And with our testimony, they can put all those people from the bar in jail. And what about your kid sister? Those same people who sold you can just as easily sell her. You want to leave Enrique out there to set up another cantina for her to work in? Oh, and one more thing, once they convict those guys for trafficking, you get a real nice apology from the American government. It's called a visa. That means you can stay in America!"

Maria kept at it well into the second hour. Finally the agent returned to Lupita's bedside. He could see Maria had continued to wear her down, but he could also see that Lupita seemed more lighthearted than just a little while ago. Finally, Maria stopped talking.

In the awkward silence, the agent carefully chanced to say something. "So," he asked Lupita quietly, "will you help us keep Enrique in jail?"

She sat staring into the distance, seeing only April's face and wishing she'd been able to do something real to save her from the whole nightmare. Looking up at the agent, she nodded as the tears came once more.

POSTSCRIPT
WHY THIS BOOK?

In the famous children's book *Where the Wild Things Are*, the second-most important character in the book—Max's mother—is never seen nor heard from. Such is the case in this book. The missionaries in *Traffic*, like many others around the world, focus on revealing Christ's love by entering a world many of us would rather not know about. Through their obedience to Christ's call in their lives, these servants work in silence and solitude to pursue the callings He has placed in their hearts, and because of their obedience God adds to His body of believers around the world every day.

CALL TO ACTION

Did you know?

- There are 27 million slaves in the world today.
- Slavery is a supply and demand issue.
- Slaves work in fields, brothels, homes, restaurants, etc.
- The average cost for a slave is $90.
- The average age of entry into prostitution is between 11 and 14.
- 1 in 5 pornographic images is of a minor.
- 244,000 minors in the United States are at a high risk of becoming slaves each year.

Resources:

- Living Mission Vol. 1: Forgotten People, NMI's mission education curriculum, published in 2010. Included in this kit are lessons, videos, podcasts, take-away sheets, and additional links to Web sites on human trafficking and how the Church of the Nazarene is responding.

- Facebook Causes: TSTOP—Texas Sex Trafficking Obliteration Project:
  <www.causes.com/tstop>
- Houston Rescue & Restore Coalition:
  <www.houstonrr.org>
- Stop Child Trafficking Now:
  <www.sctnow.org>
- Polaris Project Action Center:
  <http://actioncenter.polarisproject.org/>
- Setting Captives Free:
  <www.settingcaptivesfree.com> (online courses to help people find freedom from habitual sins like pornography, alcohol, and drug addictions)
- Free the Slaves: **<www.freetheslaves.net>**
- International Justice Mission: **<www.ijm.org>**
- US Department of Justice:
  <www.justice.gov/olp/human_trafficking. htm>

Contact us:

Darrell MacLearn (Anti-Trafficking Project Mgr, CWA-TX)

Email: tstop@cwfa.org

www.twitter.com/enddemand

Phone: 972.369.3394

To report sex trafficking, call the national hotline at 1-888-3737-888.

Bruce Nuffer

Bruce got his start in the publishing industry as the children's mission editor for the International Church of the Nazarene. Today he is responsible for running The House Studio in Kansas City.

Darrell MacLearn

Darrell MacLearn is a fourth-generation Nazarene pastor. He holds a master of arts degree in theology and has served as a pastor since 1994 in Oregon, New Mexico, and now Texas. The last few years he's been a missionary church planter launching a network of organic or simple churches that focus on building relationships and serv-

ing the community. Darrell also works with New Church Specialties as a national coach and consultant for church leaders desiring to plant nontraditional churches and start organic-type ministries. In addition to this, for the past two years he has served as the Anti-Trafficking Project Manager for Concerned Women for America—Texas, where he oversees a campaign to end the demand for human trafficking in Texas and beyond. Darrell, his wife, and two daughters reside in McKinney, Texas.